HEFTED TO THE HOWGILLS

A Year on a
Yorkshire Dales Farm

HEFTED TO THE HOWGILLS:

A Year on a Yorkshire Dales Farm

Andrea Meanwell
with photographs by Bill Robertson

HAYLOFT PUBLISHING LTD

Published Hayloft Publishing Ltd., 2020
© Andrea Meanwell, 2020

A CIP catalogue record for this book is available from the British Library.

ISBN 978-1-910237-56-4

Hayloft policy is to use papers that are natural, renewable and recyclable
products and made from wood grown in sustainable forests. The logging
and manufacturing processes are expected to conform to the
environmental regulations of the country of origin.

Designed, printed and bound in the UK and EU

Hayloft Publishing Ltd,
a company registered in England number 4802586
Low Cairndoon, Whithorn, Newton Stewart,
Dumfries & Galloway, DG8 8NF

For every new book published, Hayloft commits to plant a tree, chosen by
the author, in a new 'Wood of Words'. The woodland will capture carbon
throughout its life and help to replace that used in the production and
printing process.

Email: books@hayloft.eu
Tel: 07971 352473
www.hayloft.eu

Frontispiece: Rest and be Thankful, Howgill Fells

*For the shepherds of Cumberland, Westmorland
and Lancashire North of the Sands
Past, present and future*

Contents

The shorter and the plainer the better

Beatrix Potter on writing

Prologue

Someone had left a light on downstairs and it was lighting up the road outside the house. As I lay in bed with my husband, Antony, sleeping beside me I watched the huge snowflakes drifting down in front of the windows of the bedroom. I propped myself up with my pillows so that I could get a better view. It was magical scene, the snowflakes looked as big as dinner plates and were falling thick and fast, but it brought impending doom.

Life would be hard with the farm under several inches of snow. It would be extra work for me feeding sheep and keeping them safe. Doubtless there would be deaths. Nevertheless, I accepted that snow would come in winter, it was coming now and there was nothing I could do to stop it so I might as well enjoy watching the snow falling. We have to work with nature not fight against it on a hill farm, and it will always provide challenges.

It was more or less exactly a year since we had bought the farm, that year is chronicled in my book *Four Seasons on a Westmorland Farm*. The year had brought many challenges, mostly concerning the extreme weather during 2018. We were now embarking on our second year on the farm, attempting to make the farm profitable and 'future proof' it for the next generation. The trouble is that there is no such thing as a 'future proof farm', and a profitable hill farm is as rare as hen's teeth.

January 2019

In January you must take the time to remind yourself why you love hill farming. It is not an easy month to be outdoors looking after animals in an upland environment. What is it, then, that makes my heart sing about hill farming?

The first thing is that I love the environment in Cumbria, and the way in which it has been created and is maintained by farming. The interaction of our hardy breeds of native animals and the beauty of the Cumbrian upland environment created by them is a source of endless wonder to me.

The second thing is that I love the way my family and other families have a deep connection to the countryside, going back through countless generations. We farm with optimism that the next generation will be there to take over. We only have a short blink of an eye custodianship of our farm. The farm was here long before us, and God willing it will be here for generations after us.

I love the way that we work together as a family with complementary skills. Some of us look after the landscape, managing the grass and optimising our use of it, some collect wood and keep us warm over winter, some cook fantastic food to keep us going during good days and bad. Above all we work as a team, a family unit. We may not always see eye to eye, but at the end of the day we run one business and we all live under one roof.

My main joy in farming is the production of healthy,

happy animals. To produce a puppy or a lamb that goes on to become a member of the flock or a much loved family pet, gives me enormous pleasure. Above all, I have a love of animals. That is central to everything. An animal is not a commodity or a possession, it is a member of a team and its needs must be met, its happiness and purposefulness assured.

Reminding myself of my love of the connection to the land, my family business and the animals we farm is not an optional exercise in January, it is absolutely crucial, because otherwise it might be difficult to get up in the morning and face another day in the ice and snow.

The snow fell quickly this year and after one night of snow falling everything was blanketed in drifts and inaccessible to the outside world. Gritters and snow ploughs worked, going backwards and forwards on the motorway through the valley to keep one lane open. I could see the lights flashing, but few cars were travelling because the motorway was closed further north.

There was no question of getting to school so my fifteen-year-old son became the driver of the Land Rover for the morning. We loaded it up with hay, sheep cake and sacks of carrots and set off to see how far we could get checking the sheep.

We could get to the small rare breed sheep, and the younger shearlings in the Land Rover, but we could not get to the older sheep because of the depth of the snow. The sky was brilliantly blue and clear, and soon everything began to freeze. The snow became treacherously slippy and so we walked to check the rest of the animals. Normally the sheep just eat our own silage bales, but in this weather we gave them some sheep nuts and also put out some tubs of molasses for them to lick for energy.

The temperature at night got down to -12 degrees Celsius, and so there was no question of the snow melting. It is very difficult to work in such weather, as the ground is so icy it is difficult to drive about with food for the animals, as well as feeling very cold yourself. The sheep survive remarkably well in cold weather, they are bred for such extremities. Our Welsh Mountain sheep love to dig under the snow and find grass, despite the fact that there is a plentiful supply of silage.

We were determined to make our farm profitable, and had recently collected six 'bucket calves' from a dairy farm. These are calves from a dairy mother and a beef father, and look like any other cow bred for beef. We had these tiny charges in the sheep shed, being fed on buckets of warm milk. Their father was an Aberdeen Angus bull, and there were three boys and three girls. The idea was that we would sell the three boys when they were grown, to cover costs, and keep the three girls as breeding cows.

Hopefully they would get to know us and trust us. Two of the girls certainly did already, after a couple of days of being with us they would stand for ages while I stroked them and rubbed their heads. I worried about them in the cold temperatures, but they were fine snuggled into the straw in the sheep shed.

Pegg the Border collie had also had a litter of six puppies and they were living in the sheep shed. They had a heat lamp over them day and night as it was so cold. The landscape looked stunningly beautiful, but it made for hard work. My son Hector skidded on ice one morning and wrote his car off going into a hedge. Thankfully nobody was hurt. The fan belt snapped in the Land Rover that he was using instead, and he had to get the breakdown company to take it to a garage. The battery flattened on the tractor and he had to charge that up each time before going anywhere. Everything was being tested by the weather; man, animal and machine.

The photos that I was posting to social media made the farm look beautiful. I was of course posting photos of the landscape, and it was impossible for photos to illustrate how testing the snow and freezing temperatures really were. A daytime television show contacted me to say that they wanted to do an outside broadcast with me feeding the sheep, then nipping back into the farmhouse to get a shepherd's pie out of the oven.

I replied that I was happy for them to film me feeding the sheep to promote British farming, but the nearest sheep were about ¾ mile from a road, it was forecast to be -12 degrees Celsius on the day that they wanted to come, and we would then have to walk back to the farmhouse. I didn't want them filming in my 1960s kitchen with orange and brown lino, and ancient cooker, so I was not too bothered when they did not reply again.

The snow remained for eight days. Every morning there seemed to be a new layer of powder on top of the frozen snow. Icicles twelve inches long hung from crags where normally water must trickle. It really was a winter wonderland. When the weather is like this there is no energy left to do anything other then essential jobs. Feeding the animals, defrosting water pipes and carrying water to those whose water is frozen occupies the whole day.

Throughout it all we had one casualty, one ancient Herdwick sheep that may have died anyway, it may have just been her time to go. The shepherd has to be philosophical about these things. Every day must be endured. Every day is a day closer to April and lambing, and spring. The thought of spring is like a mirage to keep you on track, longing for magical long hot days in the sun. We know that spring is coming, so we can endure winter.

One advantage of the snowy weather was that it became easy to see animal tracks and work out what wildlife was living on the farm. Generally there was a fresh dusting of snow on top of the frozen snow each night, and we could clearly see the tracks that had been made during the night.

There were a lot of fox tracks, many more than I would have expected. It was very interesting to see the routes that they had taken, and to see that two foxes had walked side by side in my quad tracks from the allotment to the old ruined farm at Low Park.

There were also a great many roe deer tracks, criss crossing the fields and looking like they had been made at great speed. If it is possible to tell from the tracks, and the spacing of the footprints, it looked like the foxes had been plodding along, finding it quite difficult in the deep snow.

There were relatively few birds around in January, the two resident ravens sat on their customary fence posts and watched the quad go by. Crows swooped around where I fed the sheep their hay, and then landed to eat hayseeds that had fallen through the hayrack.

Our most exciting wildlife sighting was an ermine stoat. I had noticed that something had been burrowing in and out of a small dry stone wall in the back garden, and Ruby

15

my Lancashire heeler kept sniffing the hole. One morning my son saw it bounding about in the garden, completely white except for the tip of its tail which was black.

The stoat's coat turns white in snowy weather so that it is camouflaged in the snow. It is probably no coincidence that it was living next to where my hens liked to lay their eggs in an old outhouse where they had made a nest from fallen leaves, as stoats love to eat eggs.

Historically their white fur was highly prized, and during the reign of Edward III in England (1327-77) ermine was only allowed to be worn by members of the royal family. State robes were also made in such a way that the positions of the dark spots (tails) could tell you the rank of the wearer.

Bringing cheer throughout January were thousands and thousands of snowdrops in the farmhouse garden and hedgerows. It is not an exaggeration to say that the walled garden looked like in was covered in snow for the whole month because of the numbers of flowers. Even in bleakest January, nature does its best to cheer us up.

Rest and Be Thankful

Half way
On my shepherding rounds
I have a gate that I stop at
I call it my
'Rest and Be Thankful'

I pull the water bottle
Out from under the quad's rack
And sit drinking in the view
Every day the same view
Every day I'm thankful

The hills overlap
In the distance
Like a child's drawing
Interlocking with the river
Weaving its way through

Every day the view changes
Thunderclouds darken the fells
Or snow makes them clean
Sometimes brown and dead
Sometimes green and alive

From my rest stop
I can see Norman's farm
High Carlingill across the valley
Another working farm
The only dwelling in sight

I derive great comfort
From knowing someone is there
I am not entirely alone
In this vast landscape
It's still a working landscape

Thankfully some of us are still here
Still working, still drinking in the view
I am part of something bigger
There are other sheep, other shepherds
Not close at hand, but not far away

The gatepost at the
Rest and Be Thankful gate
Has a miniature world on the top
A jungle made of moss
With insects in its boughs

I can stretch my eyes
To Carlingill or beyond
Or I can focus on the tiny
Miraculous miniature world
Both are within reach

Our shepherding world
May seem vast to us
But it is only a tiny gatepost world
In the grand scheme of things
And somebody may choose
To knock that gatepost down

Febuary

When the thaw came at the beginning of February it was a relief to see that things had survived under the snow. The snowdrops still looked resplendent in their almost luminous white petals, and daffodils were beginning to shoot up in the garden and along the roadsides.

Despite all this horticultural activity February seemed to have somewhat of an avian theme this year. The first upsetting incident with a bird was finding a dead barn owl on a bale of straw in the sheep shed. It had no signs of injury and I assumed, rightly or wrongly, that it had starved due to lack of food in the snow and ice.

It gave me an opportunity to have a close look at the beautiful bird, and I was particularly enamoured with its wing feathers. Humans think they are talented at pattern design, but the wings of the owl were more amazing to me than any work of art.

A pair of breeding oystercatchers that had spent last year on the farm returned to nest by the riverbank, and I grew accustomed to seeing their bright orange beaks every morning as I drove past on the quad.

Another bird that we had a closer encounter with than we would have expected was a buzzard. My son Hector found it with its head stuck between the narrow rails of a Network Rail fence, and freed it. He came bursting into the kitchen carrying the buzzard under his arm like a tame hen shouting, "Mum look what I've found." I was absolutely astonished when I came downstairs and saw the buzzard flapping his wings and trying to escape from my son's clutches now that it had regained its composure after being trapped and subdued. We took it outside and it soared majestically away.

This was not the first encounter that we have had with a buzzard. The summer before Antony had had several run ins with one protecting a nest. The bird had taken to dive-bombing him as he approached the wood where its nest was, and Antony took to carrying a stick and wearing a hat in case it attacked him. The adult birds would regularly swoop down on him narrowly avoiding his head in a bid to keep him away from the wood where the nest was.

Our valley is supporting a great variety of wildlife, like the owls, buzzards and oystercatchers, and this belief was picked up by a Radio 4 producer who wanted to make a programme about 'crossing divides' in Britain. The aim of the programme was to show that even in 'divided Britain' today – divided by the issue of whether to leave the European Union or not, there can be common ground in opposing points of view.

Other 'crossing divides' episodes have been made about 4 x 4 drivers on green lanes, graffiti, and cyclists and cars. I agreed to discuss rewilding with Lee Schofield from the RSPB who manages a large area near Haweswater in the Lake District National Park owned by United Utilities. Lee has a keen interest in conservation, and I knew that we would have many beliefs in common. Farmers who care for the natural landscape and conservationists are often portrayed as being in opposition by the media, but actually

have many beliefs in common.

The term 'rewilding' has served to divide the two camps rather than bringing them together in the public's perception of farming and wildlife. High profile figures such as George Monbiot have fuelled this belief that the uplands of Britain are 'sheepwrecked'.

I agreed to do the radio discussion, to be recorded in our farm kitchen, and was then told that a video of the discussion was then going to be made for the BBC Sounds App. I'm always reluctant to appear on film, but having gone this far it was too late to change my mind. So on the appointed bleak, cold day in February the producer and filmmaker arrived at the farm.

As well as filming the discussion they also filmed me feeding sheep, and strolling around the farm talking to Lee. On one shot Lee and I are standing contemplating a desperately bleak looking valley in the grip of winter, and an old silage wrap was caught in a tree above our heads. It had blown up into the tree and was too high for me to reach, having seen the video I wish I had made more of an effort to get it down.

The programme aired a couple of days later when Hector and I were ear-tagging lambs in the sheep shed. In order to hear it clearly I took my phone and sat down with the puppies in the corner of the shed. We all listened intently. I was actually amazed at how much I said. It seemed to make sense, and I was quite happy with the result. I am always keen to emphasise the value that I see in hill farming, the benefits to wildlife and the high quality food that we produce. It is difficult to put yourself forward as a spokesperson for your profession, but I think it went well.

I gave the producer of the radio programme a list of ideas for programmes for the future, one of which he says he will definitely pitch to Radio 4. I would like to hear more programmes about farming during the day on the radio, not just very early in the morning on *Farming Today*, which I imagine only farmers hear.

We need to do all we can to engage the public with our profession. People need us to produce their food, and we need them to support British farming.

The day after the radio programme was broadcast I was brought back down to reality with a bump. It was the day that our Tb tests would be read. The cows had all been injected with bovine and avian Tb to see if they would react to them. As we waited in the farmyard for the vet to arrive a toad ambled his way across the yard, a sure sign that spring was on the way.

The cattle have had several Tb tests in the last couple of years, and this one was because we had moved farms and so are classified as a new herd. All the cows had had several tests before and so I had no need to be anxious or concerned about the results.

The last cow to go through the crush was Bluebell. She wears 001 in her ear as she was the first cow that I ever bred. (There is a picture of me sitting with her in *A Native Breed*). The vet who had come from Sicily to do Tb tests looked frozen on this winter's day, and he sighed and looked at me and then at the cow.

"Hector," I shouted, and my son was quickly at the side of the crush. "There are definitely lumps" said the vet, Hector got into the crush with the cow and lifted her head up so that the vet could measure the lumps accurately. The

Dexters are so tiny that it is sometimes difficult to get them held securely in a full sized crush.

"Inconclusive" was the verdict, so Bluebell had to be isolated from the herd until April when another test could be done. The vet got out his calendar and said that he would be back on 20 April to test again – 20 April was also the day on which Bluebell's first calf was due to be born. It was going to be a difficult wait.

I could not leave Bluebell on her own for two months, so I put 007 (James Bond) in with her. If Bluebell had Tb the chances were that James Bond would also catch it, but he was a calf being reared for meat that was almost ready to go. He was now fulfilling another role as a companion animal. We must always make sure that we are kind and consider the animal's welfare as well as our own business outcomes. Cows are sociable animals and no cow would like to be alone for two months, plus Bluebell and James Bond had always got on well.

If we were found to have Tb in April it would have implications for our business and for our neighbours as well who would have to have additional Tb tests. We had to hope that it did not come to that.

There were thankfully some sunny days in February to gather in our sheep and vaccinate them six weeks before lambing was due to begin. They had been scanned by a mobile scanner and all had marks with the number of lambs that they were expecting on their backs. Red for no lambs, nothing for one lamb, a green dot for twins and two green dots for triplets.

We had never before had a sheep expecting triplets, and we had eleven this year. This served to emphasis how we had 'steeped up' our farming operation. Some sheep evaded capture for the scanner, and we did not scan the rare breeds, but we scanned 247 sheep and they scanned at average of 158%. This meant that on average each sheep was expecting 1.58 lambs. Those who were not carrying lambs were turned away to rough grazing if they were shearlings – around 18 months old. If they were older than that they were sold.

The daily routine in February is one of feeding. The ewes are two months away from giving birth and we must make sure that they have enough silage at all times. The ones having two or more lambs are also given a bit of concentrated feed. We have to buy this in, and we plan to produce stubble turnips ourselves next year to feed them on. This will make our farm more sustainable. The turnips will be eaten while they are growing in the ground, and then the ewes will not need to consume any bought in food.

During February I sold my Ouessant boy lambs from the previous year as pets to smallholders, and we began to sell our fattened commercial lambs. We had sold our lambs 'store' at weaning at our previous farm, getting between twenty six and nineteen pounds for them. We calculated that it had cost us twelve pounds extra per lamb to keep them until now, and were pleased when they sold for seventy pounds each. The cost of producing the lamb until weaning was twenty six pounds each, plus twelve pounds each after weaning, meaning each lamb cost thirty eight pounds to produce. If we can sell them at seventy pounds each we have a chance of our farm business being profitable.

The sheep that were scanned were expecting 390 lambs.

Around 60 of these will be kept as flock replacements, so we will have a lot of lambs to fatten next year. Knowing we can do this profitably was a great boost to our confidence.

Opening the cheque from the auction I looked out of the kitchen window and thought, "We can actually do this". That optimism, however, was about to take a serious battering during what was a very eventful month of March.

A Champagne Moment

Thousands of people pass
Through our valley every day
In cars and lorries on the M6
And in trains on
The West Coast mainline

Thousands of people
Whizzing through our farm
And yet, I have no contact
No conversation
With a single soul

The train line is parallel
To where I drive on the quad
But the carriages are angled
So that I cannot see
The people on board

Steam trains sometimes
Use the main line
Travelling slower
Taking in the view
On an excursion

The carriages are
Designed differently
I can see the people
On the trains
And they can see me

On the bleakest of
February days
I was three miles from home
Next to the railway line
Ankle deep in mud

I was surrounded
By jostling sheep
Pushing and nearly
Knocking me over
Trying to get food

The quad has stopped
In the thick mud
It will not start again
The rain was pouring down
And tears rolled down my cheeks

Alongcame a steam train
And I looked up into
Another world
Time seemed to stand still
As the train chugged past

A man was standing
Looking out of the window
Opening a bottle of champagne
At a table with glasses
And white linen napkins

We made eye contact
Me crying in the rain
And him posed to pop the cork
He looked as if to say
"What is wrong?"

But then the train
Had gone.
And I was alone
Three miles from home
In the rain.

March

The first of March should have been a happy day of celebration. It was my parents Golden Wedding Anniversary. Initially I had been booked on a course about injecting glucose into newborn lambs that were struggling, but Dad had asked me to cancel it because he wanted to have a special anniversary meal on the day itself.

It had been quite wet and the river that runs through the farm was quite deep. When I drove down to check the sheep on the quad bike I was quite shocked to see a dead sheep in the middle of the river. I stood on the edge of the river and began to wade in, but it was going to knock me off my feet so I had to come back. It is illegal to leave a dead sheep in the river, so I stood for a while wondering what I should do and concluded I would have to leave it there until the river level went down. I couldn't get near to the body to see what was wrong with the sheep, or work out why it had ventured into the river. Even blind sheep that get 'windblown' eye problems are not usually prone to wandering into water.

I left the sheep and drove up the hill. The next strange thing was that large numbers of the sheep were pushing themselves into the green railings at the top of the field. Very few sheep were actually grazing; they were all standing together at the top. Around the gateway the ground was all poached. It looked as if they had all stood together in a big group all night.

I was now beginning to get really alarmed, and got up to the top of the hill to look at the sheep. None of them moved, they all stood there looking at me like rabbits in car headlights. It took my brain about half a minute to compute what was going on, and then I looked away from their faces and onto their bodies and realised that some of them were very badly injured. They had huge open wounds around their bottoms, big gaping holes in their flesh the size of my hand.

I gasped, in shock with the breath taken out of me, and got onto the phone. Hector was working on another farm. Thankfully he answered.

"Hector, you need to come home. Something has been attacking the sheep."

"How do you know?"

"They've got big open wounds as big as my hands. They're all stood up against the fence. Honestly, its like a scene from a horror movie."

We agreed that he would come home, and I went back home to get a trailer to bring the injured sheep home in. As I got back into the yard a neighbour appeared in his car. As he opened the car door to talk to me I burst into tears

"Oh its horrible. Something has been attacking my sheep. They've got big open wounds on them."

As my neighbour took in what I had just said, Hector came flying into the yard in his pick up. He jumped out of the pick up and gave me a hug. A rare moment of mother/son physical affection – he is not normally one for hugging. Then we sprang into action getting the trailer fixed on.

The injured sheep from the first field were brought home, and we phoned a neighbour whose dogs had previously attacked our sheep to ask where his dogs were. He was on holiday, and said that his dogs should be chained up in the yard. Hector drove down to his farm and they were not chained up in the yard.

It was now a matter of urgency to find the dogs before they attacked any more sheep. I stayed at home with the injured sheep cleaning their wounds and applying first aid, and getting them settled into a pen on straw. They were very shocked. I did not know if they would survive.

Hector went off around the farm, and unfortunately came back with a trailer load of dead sheep that he had found in various fields, including my former pet lamb "Muley" that I had fed from a day old and who was expecting twins, and two of my girls from my original flock bought in 2015. For four years these two girls had quietly minded their own business and bred good lambs. Now they had been eaten alive. They had never harmed anyone in their gentle lives. It absolutely broke my heart to see the pile of dead sheep accumulating.

To cut a long story short, as it is rather traumatic to tell, the dogs were still at large and we had to get someone to come over and shoot them. This again broke my heart. I had a litter of beautiful border collie puppies in the sheep shed, and we were having to get somebody to shoot dogs on our land.

It was an horrific, difficult day. We than had to dash out for the special meal for my parent's wedding anniversary. Dad had been texting to ask why we had not set off yet. I sat in the restaurant in a trance, wondering what was happening at home. I didn't tell my parents that we had to shoot the dogs. I didn't expect shepherding to be so emotionally traumatic.

We called the police to tell them what had happened. They came round and looked at the scene and said that we were justified in shooting the dogs. That didn't really make me feel any better about it. The insurance assessor wanted to study the dead sheep, so they were piled up in the yard for a few days. They must have been visible from the train as a friend phoned to ask what was gong on and why we had a big pile of dead sheep in the yard. What was going on was that we were all in shock.

Thankfully I had the joy of the puppies to distract me,

and people arriving to meet them and choose a puppy for their family. It is always a pleasure to provide a family with a much loved family pet with a temperament that suits their lifestyle.

There were two other arrivals in the farm yard, two pigs from a friend's litter. We would use these as a source of our own food. My two younger sons eat a tremendous amount of sausage and bacon, and I would rather that they ate our own bacon than shop bought without an identifiable source. We are lucky in that we have Tebay Services close by where we can buy locally produced meat, but we are also in the fortunate position of being able to produce our own eggs and meat.

At the bottom of our farm were some ancient woodlands that are primarily alder and wych elm. In order to try and understand our woodlands a little better I went on a day course about understanding Atlantic Woodlands run by the charity Plantlife. It was a very informative but utterly mind boggling day with the sheer number of lichens observed. At the end of the day I had learnt a little about lichen, but I think in order to have a good understanding of lichen is probably a lifetime's work. At least I could now recognise a few common lichens, and would not confuse them with mosses. Any future understanding would have to wait for another year.

As spring plants began to flower around the farm I made a point of photographing them and recording the different species. This information may be crucial in future years if the structure of government subsidies changes when we leave the European Union. The government is currently trialling a new system of environmental land management schemes, and payments may be 'by results'. In this case it will be a great advantage to know what is already growing on the farm.

The mind-set of farming in the uplands may have to change if the farmer wants to receive subsidy. Not only will we be producing a food product (meat) we will also be de-livering environmental 'public goods' – as yet to be defined but probably plants, wildlife species, clean air and water, carbon sequestration and public access – none of which is easy to put a value on or quantify the amount on a farm. Farmers in the uplands should be well placed to deliver these goods, particularly those in national parks, as long as they have the inclination and the knowledge required to record them.

Meanwhile we had work with the current schemes, and we were pleased to receive a Countryside Stewardship agreement for the area around Low Borrowbridge Farm including some drystone walling, hedging and fencing off riparian strips. There wasn't much time to complete the work before the birds started nesting, so Hector set to hedging almost immediately, laying the hedgerows traditionally in the Westmorland style after a couple of hours tuition from a neighbour.

This scheme is an excellent way for us to farm traditionally for the benefit of wildlife habitats on the farm, and for us to be paid to do so. Before long the hedges were laid and ready for birds to nest in this coming season. Walls were rebuilt when Hector found himself with a couple of hours to spare. The whole place was looking tidier.

With the fencing we would not receive the full cost of a contractor coming to put up fencing for us, but we decided to ask a contractor to do it, as we wanted it to be an excellent job. Unfortunately everybody locally seemed to be receiving their agreements at the same time, and we would have to wait a while for the contractor to do it for us.

On some days Hector and I worked together on the farm, and on other days he worked on a different farm and I worked alone. Throughout March our main job was

checking the pregnant sheep and cows. We would go together on the quad bike with the trailer attached, in case we
needed to bring back any casualties to the farm yard. Hector would drive while I sat on the back of the quad on a
wooden seat on the rear rack.

Following on from the sheep attack I had not been feeling well, and one morning was feeling quite queasy sitting
on the back of the quad. It didn't help that it had been relentlessly wet and the quad was sliding about a lot. When
we got to the allotment I felt that I was going to be sick, so
I said to Hector that I would get off the quad and walk to

the bottom meadow to check the sheep. He could drive around checking the sheep at the top and then drive down to the bottom. It was quite a steep hill, when we first moved to the farm it had taken me a while to build up the courage to drive down it, and Hector had hammered some red posts into the hillside to mark the safe route.

I walked down to the bottom meadow, and found a sheep that did not look too bright. I thought he should bring her closer to home to keep an eye on her, so I phoned Hector and asked him to come and pick us up. I stood next to the steep hillside and waited for him to appear at the top.

What I saw next was not what I expected, and it took a while for me to comprehend what had happened. First of all the quad came over the hill. It was like a scene from the *Italian Job* where the sports cars roll down the mountainside and are smashed to pieces. I stood watching the quad come over the top and counted that it rolled six times. In the *Italian Job* I was always disappointed that some of the cars slid and did not roll. No such disappointment today. It rolled six times and then came to an abrupt stop in a peat bog. I stood, transfixed, unable to move.

Next the quad trailer came over the hill on its own. It rolled three times and slid down next to the quad. There was no sign of Hector. I knew that if I had been driving I would not have jumped off quickly and probably would have been seriously injured. Where was he? Had he been squashed under the quad? I stood in shock, unable to move.

After what seemed like a lifetime a figure appeared at the top of the hill looking over

"Are you OK?" I shouted. He was silhouetted against the grey sky.

"The quad!" he shouted.

"Never mind the quad, are you injured?" I shouted.

"No" he replied, and was soon down on the bottom meadow. The quad was rapidly sinking into a peat bog.

"Quick" he said, "we have to stop the peat from swallowing up the quad." We both worked together with all our strength to lift the quad. He was pushing the front up and I was lifting the tow bar.

Some of the plastic panels had been broken off. The handlebars were bent at a funny angle. The brakes were snapped off. We lifted the quad up out of the bog and attached the trailer. Hector pressed the ignition button and remarkably it started.

We drove home, had a cup of tea, and assessed the situation. It could definitely have been worse. Hector decided to immediately take the quad to the local dealership, as it would be needed at lambing time. He put it into the small sheep trailer. The trailer had just come back from being repaired after the wheel bearings had collapsed. He set off quickly to try and get it to the dealership before it closed.

I was in the kitchen boxing up some eggs when the phone rang. It was Hector on hands free in his pick up, saying that he was travelling along the main road into South Cumbria and there was smoke coming out from the trailer wheels.

"Pull over quickly" I urged him.

"No I don't want to stop or the dealership will be closed."

Then he had to stop, as the wheels burst into flames. Thankfully he was near his girlfriend's farm so he pulled into their yard, abandoned our trailer and continued with one of theirs. It was a very dramatic day and that was not the end of it, later that evening he was going back to his girlfriend's to pick up the trailer when the fan belt snapped in the Land Rover, and he had to call out the breakdown company.

We were struggling because of a combination of old and repaired machinery letting us down. I resolved to sell the Land Rover. The anxiety involved in driving it was too great. It was a liability. We needed a way to generate some more income, in order to improve our equipment and keep ourselves safe. Little did we know, a solution was about to present itself.

Winton Lambs

Passing through Winton
A team of joyful lambs
Decide to race my car
In the evening sun

Their little black
Swaledale faces bobbing
Up and down along
The wall to the corner

It is a timeless scene
And suddenly I remember
That my ancestors
Used to live on this farm

Three hundred years ago
These very fields
Were tended by my family
Of yeoman farmers

I bet they watched
Their racing lambs
On this very spot
On just such a spring evening

I fall through time for a moment
I am the farmer here
These are my lambs
This is my home

And then I am back in
The Land Rover
Driving home…
Back to 2019

April

April is, and always will be, all about lambing. Our tups had been released so that lambing should start on the 5 April, and we knew from the way in which the sheep had been marked after tupping that they should mostly lamb within fourteen days.

We had the sheep split into separate groups after they had been scanned. The older ewes had scanned at 158% (1.58 lambs/ewe) and the shearlings at 135%. There were eleven ewes expecting triplets, and they were in a little field close to home so that they could have additional feed. The twins were in one group of about 100 ewes, and they would be moved closer to home to keep an eye on them, the remainder that were having a single lamb would lamb on the 'far meadows' a short distance from home.

On the 1st April we walked the sheep closer to home into the fields that we wanted them ready for lambing. The twin carrying ewes came into the meadows around home. We walked them halfway from Low Park, and then left them there to rest for a couple of hours, then finished the journey home. On the way back towards home, within sight of the meadows, one ewe's water bag burst. I walked slowly behind her as she waddled into the field and gave birth to a set of twins in quick succession. Lambing had begun.

We had four days until the rest of the ewes were due to start lambing, so pushed ourselves to finish the hedging

jobs for our Countryside Stewardship scheme. Once lambing really began it would be relentlessly busy. I set about
putting up the pens in the sheep shed in case any sheep
needed to come indoors, and set up the 'shepherdess' milk
machine ready for any lambs needing extra milk.

The Ouessants were brought inside to lamb. These tiny
sheep do not lamb outside as crows have a habit of dive
bombing their tiny lambs and trying to eat their eyes.
Hopefully every other ewe would lamb outside.

I also arranged for the farrier to come just before lambing was due to begin, as I knew that I would not be able to
wander far from home. Thankfully all the ponies had win-
tered well and there were no problems with their feet.

Now that I had decided to sell my Land Rover Defender
there was no going back on the decision. Thankfully it was
seen as very desirable by many garages and I was able to
trade it in for a Land Rover Freelander with only a little
money to make up the difference in the prices. On the last
day of having it I drove the Defender right up onto the
Howgill fells and took some lovely photos of it. It certainly
looked good in the photos. It might be the last time that I
drove one of these iconic vehicles, but I breathed a sigh of
relief when I drove out of the garage in the Freelander with
a warranty the following morning.

Hector finished his hedging, but was not getting much
time to get on with his walling and fencing as he had to
spend so much time on other farms. I was very busy putting
together a Countryside Stewardship application for the riparian strips down to Low Park. This would involve fencing off about two and a half miles of riverbank for wildlife
habitats.

One day while we were having our lunch I saw a job advertised – Farming Officer with The Lake District National Park. I read out the job description to Hector who said

"Go for it Mum." It seemed the ideal job; to help raise the profile of shepherding in the World Heritage Site. The advert asked, "Can you enable a strong farming voice to help shape the future of the Lake District?"

"Yes," I thought, "I think I could."

A discussion with Hector made clear that he was all for

the idea. I would apply for the job and if successful we would do a swap – I would go out to work and he would stay on the farm. It made financial sense too, as the job paid double what Hector could hope to earn. We had recently set up a partnership, and it appeared that it would be beneficial for the partnership for me to apply for the job. Succession from myself to Hector was going to happen one day, perhaps sooner than we had expected.

I put in my application, as ever, from the heart. At the end of the application I wrote 'nothing is more important to me than keeping hefted flocks on the Lake District fells.' I re-read the application, and as I was borrowing my Antony's laptop I thought it would be prudent to add in the word 'professionally', so that it read that nothing was more important to me professionally, then I sent it off.

The following day, the last day before lambing was due to begin, I travelled over to Eskdale in the west of the Lake District to interview a young couple who had recently taken on the tenancy of a National Trust farm. The article was for Cumbria magazine. Once on the farm I was struck by how clear sighted Beatrix Potter had been in her vision to protect the hefted flocks of Herdwick sheep in the Lake District. She wasn't from the Lake District but she clearly understood the heart of the culture of the area and did all she could to preserve it. If I got the job as farming officer I could do worse than take her as my inspiration.

Meanwhile I found inspiration in the many plants and flowers that started busting into life. The slopes around the farm were an absolute vision of blue as the bluebells began to flower. It was a spectacular year for hawthorn and bluebells. The blue and white was crisp and luminous against the green grass.

The weather was set fair, the grass was growing and the sheep were ready to lamb. Everything was ready as the first lambs began to arrive – usually either first thing in the morning or last thing at night. Our policy was definitely to let the sheep get on with it and intervene as little as possible. All the sheep except the Ouessants were outdoors. We assembled our 'lamb adopter' to use just in case a sheep rejected a lamb. This is an old wooden structure where the sheep's head is fastened at one end so that she cannot barge her lamb away if the lamb wants to feed. Generally after a couple of feeds she will then settle down and accept that she has a lamb.

What a lambing time we had! The weather was definitely on our side (for once). Lambs were born quickly, without trouble, and were soon running about in the sunshine. There were some problem cases – prolapsed uteruses in the main. We had to do some adopting and swapping around of lambs as a couple of lambs were born dead, but we managed to adopt two lambs from triplets onto these ewes. It all seemed to work out perfectly with the timing of triplets being born.

If a sheep has triplets she doesn't have enough milk to feed three lambs (especially as our grass quality is very poor as we are an upland farm), so one is removed immediately at birth. The orphan lamb is then taken inside and adopted onto a ewe that has lost her lamb in the lamb adopter. Sometimes we remove the dead lamb's skin and tie it around the adopted lamb, on other occasions the ewe is desperate for a lamb and is happy to take any lamb as her own. It is a system that works well, and we ended up with very few lambs being fed on powdered milk long term.

Hector and I got into a routine where I checked the sheep at about midnight before going to bed, and he got up at 6am and checked them then. The evenings were warm and balmy, and often I walked around the fields in my pyjamas with my head torch on checking the sheep.

It was an enjoyable work, a life that we had dreamed of. At the end of April I received an invitation to go for an interview at the head office of the Lake District National Park. The interview was to be held on the 3 May, and I was to do a presentation about how I would 'establish and develop relationships within the Lake District Farming Community and other stakeholders in order to help facilitate action to address issues and maximise opportunities.' The idea of a new role was becoming very real.

Also very real was the threat of Tb. On the day that she was due to calf, the vet came to retest Bluebell. I could see that she definitely had lumps on her neck, but the vet said that these were within the allowed size. I was so relieved that she didn't have Tb that I did a little song and dance routine across the farmyard – much to Bluebell's bemusement.

Archive

At the auction
On a Saturday morning
I cannot resist
The paraphernalia of
Shepherding.

There are few
Tools of the trade
All well used
All well worn
Nothing for show

Shepherds guides
Flock books
Shepherds crooks
Horn burning irons
Auction catalogues

I cannot let
These items wander far
Or be left unsold
And so my house
Becomes a mini museum

Crooks stand by my
Office door
Names burnt into them
Waiting for their owners
Or market day

Shepherds guides
Line the shelves
Annotated with pencil marks
And smit smudges
Well thumbed

Flock books
Auction catalogues
Show programmes
Newsletters
Form an archive

What on earth
Am I collecting this for?
It is the archaeology
Of shepherding
In these hills

The few possessions
Marking the lives
Of shepherds past
Are gathered here
Waiting.

May

The beginning of May saw a rush of steam trains going through the gorge as they made their way north for the summer season. It was a real highlight for me to see the Union of South Africa steaming through the farm. This is a steam locomotive built in Doncaster in 1937 and was a familiar train to my grandad who was a locomotive driver. I stood on the wall top next to the railway line and watched the train steaming through the farm. I waved to the driver as he steamed past the sheep pens.

A lot of our work during May is in the sheep pens. Once the ewe and her twins are a few days old, having been born in the meadows, we walk them into the sheep pens for 'marking'. We like to have twelve sets of twins for each batch if possible.

The lambs are ear tagged if they are a possible flock replacement (a Rough Fell or Welsh Speckle gimmer lamb born 'pure' to the same breed of tup), marked with our red smit mark in case they get lost, and tailed. An elastic band is put around the end of their tail to shorten it. We decided to do this after one year when we left the tails long and a lot of the lambs got 'wicked' – maggots growing around their bottoms after a fly had laid eggs there. It was most unpleasant for them.

The ewes and the lambs are then taken in the trailer (in two compartments, six ewes and twelve lambs in each) down to Low Park Farm for the summer. It is quite a long, bumpy ride and I bet they are glad to get there. It had definitely worked better for us this year lambing at Low Borrowbridge and then moving them the three and a half miles down to Low Park, rather than lambing at both locations and whizzing between the two like last year.

It was lovely to see the ewes and the lambs under the hawthorn trees and amongst the bluebells, happily living at Low Park Farm. Two of the ewes that were badly injured in the dog attack each had a single lamb and were very pleased with them. The old sheep that was attacked by the dog the previous year also had a little lamb, even though she was not put to the tup. There must have been some wall jumping going on. It was a black spotty lamb so the father is a mystery. Wherever he came from, she was certainly very happy with her new purpose in life looking after her lamb.

Squiggle and her sister Three Dots both had gimmer lambs that can join the flock. I can't ever remember such a happy and successful lambing. The good weather played a part in this of course. It can make such a difference, between life and death.

We were getting towards the end of lambing; nearly all were down at Low Park, when calving began. The first calf to appear was out of one of the Stabiliser cows. These are beef cattle born to dairy cows that my son had bought from the farm where he worked. It was a good healthy heifer calf, and the mother was absolutely running with milk.

The next calving was not such a success. The youngest Dexter had begun to calf, and had two feet sticking out but very little sign of any progress. Hector had gone to

Blackpool for the weekend with Young Farmers, so after watching the cow for a while I reluctantly phoned him. He was home within the hour, and we went down to the field together to catch the cow, armed with a calving aid and two ropes.

Despite having had cows for about six years we had never actually had to calve a cow before. We have native breeds of cattle mostly, and they have always calved them-selves easily. We managed to walk the cow into a little area under a cliff, and she lay down to try and push the calf out. We tried to attach the ropes to the calf's feet and pull it out, but it was stuck fast. Quickly Hector attached the ropes to the calving aid, a sort of a crank, and thankfully when he wound it up the calf began to move. It was coming backwards.

We managed to get the calf out without harming the cow, but unfortunately the calf died shortly afterwards. It was very disappointing for us but the heifer did not seem to be concerned. She took no interest in the dead calf so we did not go and buy another to adopt onto her. We thought she had been through enough of an ordeal.

Shortly after this Bluebell began to calve. I had left her in the farmyard after the Tb test as she had looked like she was about to give birth at any moment. I sat in the cowshed and watched her pacing about, and the legs of the calf appeared. Thankfully the calf was coming the right way this time, but it was not coming quickly and progress was slow.

I had known Bluebell since the hour of her birth in Rusland, and she trusted me, but I knew from experience that a cow calving can be unpredictable so I phoned Hector and asked him to come to the yard. Together we tied the ropes onto the calf's feet. Hector pulled and I eased the head out with my hand. A lovely bull calf was born, and we left them alone to bond.

Later we went to check on the new calf several times, and while he was happily snuggled up next to Bluebell there was no evidence that he had had any milk. We kept checking throughout the day, and at teatime decided to give the calf a bottle. He gratefully drank the milk, and there then followed three days of tuition, both mother and baby needed help to understand how the calf was to get his milk. We had to put Bluebell into the cattle crush and encourage the calf to drink whilst she was restrained. The calf understood that the bottle contained his milk, and so Hector kept putting the bottle underneath Bluebell next to her udders and encouraging him to try the udders as well. Thankfully Bluebell accepted this with good humour and after three days they were successfully feeding by themselves without any help.

A couple of the Aberdeen Anguses had their calves successfully, and one of the Dexters had her second calf. She was actually the mother of the one that had the calf that died, and it was very interesting to watch the three of them form a family group.

It is common practice for cows to hide their calves in the rushes until they are a few days old. So it can be difficult to find them and check on them. The strategy is to approach the cow, the mother, and then watch where her eyes keep glancing over to find out where her calf is hidden. Once the calves can walk and are a few days old they join the herd. When they join the herd they are then put into a cow 'nursery' with the other calves. They all rest together and one cow will be left on duty to look after them while the others graze. They share this duty amongst themselves, and cows without a calf take a turn too. They are all good citizens.

One morning I was absolutely delighted to see that one of the Dexters had given birth to not one but two heifer calves. We have never had a cow have twins before. It was a joy to see them feeding together, although it could be quite tricky in the first few days to find them and check on them as they were so tiny.

The last of the sheep were moved off the meadows and

they were 'shut up' to grow grass to turn into hay or silage. Very annoyingly a few of the Herdwicks and their lambs did not accept that they had been moved off the meadows and kept jumping back. It was a nightmare trying to keep them out. We tried shutting them in the cow barn but they escaped from there. They really were very naughty!

I spent any spare time that I had photographing and preparing a Countryside Stewardship application for the area around Low Park Farm. I had to photograph each area of riparian strip. It was quite an undertaking getting the application together, but it was an application for £70,000 worth of funding, so I hoped that it would be worth the effort – £50,000 pounds of this was for infrastructure fencing and walling to ensure livestock did not get into the riparian area or the areas set aside for wildlife habitats.

I also had another application to focus on. I delivered my presentation about building relationships with farmers at the head office of the Lake District National Park Authority and was amazed when a couple of days later they asked me to meet up again to discuss the role. I checked with Hector that he did indeed want to return to work at home full time, and he did, and so I accepted the role of farming officer. It would be a seriously challenging role, but there was nothing more important to me than the continuance of upland farming. I would rather do the job myself and give it my best shot, than watch someone else attempt to do it.

I was nearly 50, and about to take up a new government position. I would have to learn all about their computer systems and policies, but I was determined to keep my objectives clear in my mind. Like Beatrix Potter I had the chance

Marking lambs.

to help to protect the hefted flocks of the Lake District, which were seriously jeopardised by the prospect of Brexit and the loss of the Basic Payment Scheme for farmers that had subsidised hill farms quite successfully. I would do my best to fight in the upland farmer's corner in the battle that was about to commence for the future of farming in the UK.

The Lake District was actively involved in trialling the new Environmental Land Management Schemes. It was very important that these schemes were suitable for and beneficial to upland farmers. I knew from my experience as a teacher that often schemes were designed that were entirely inappropriate for small country locations, so I was keen to get involved in these trials to try to help make them something that was appropriate for small upland farms.

I arrived at the office in my proper shoes (not wellies) and was issued with a laptop and a mobile phone. My first event was to visit 'North Sheep', an industry event as the Lake District National Park's representative. I was ready for the challenge.

Hedgepig

It's one of those long
Summer evenings
That we had in the 1970s
When you could play outside
Until it was really dark and your eyes
Just adjust to the darkness

I was sitting in
My cousin's tree house
Just some planks of wood
Up a tree
On a railway embankment
On the Settle to Carlisle line

Looking out
Into the darkness
Somehow I can see
Like a nocturnal animal
But then I heard
An unfamiliar sound

A snuffling
A sniffing
I have no idea what it is
"Stephen, Stephen"
I called to my cousin
But no one comes

No one comes so I must
Wait, petrified up a tree
In the dark on my own
A huge carnivorous animal
Is on its way
To eat me up

Then underneath
The bottom of the tree
Passes a very noisy
Hedgehog
Out looking for her breakfast
Now night has fallen

I will not mention this
To anyone,
This fear of the hedgehog
That I braved alone
And more than that
A startling discovery

We may think
That this is our farm
But other creatures
Have this as a home too
We do not own this land alone
Other creatures have a claim

Other creatures have a right
To live here
This land is a living organism
It defies ownership
It has a soul
Of its own.

I understand
That wildlife and
Farm life must co-exist
Both equally valid
Both must be respected
I discovered this myself

Late one summer
Up a tree
Abandoned by my cousin
If I hadn't been alone
Unsupervised
I would not have discovered this

Thank goodness
For the freedom
Of a 1970s summer
Are our children today
Given such freedom
To learn?

June

June began with a flurry of events. In the same week I attended North Sheep I also went to Greenholme Show. This is a traditional show in the 'extension area' of the Lake District National Park. In 2016 the Lake District and Yorkshire Dales National Parks were extended, and Greenholme Show was just over the motorway from our farm, in the Lake District extension area. Unfortunately it poured down all day at the show, but it did not dampen the enthusiasm of the shepherds showing their sheep in the classes that we were sponsoring.

The day after the show it was Open Farm Sunday. This is a national initiative to open farms to the public to reconnect people to the countryside and the farmers there who produce their food. I say 'reconnect' as there is a general belief that many people do not have a connection with the people who produce their food.

Thankfully it was a dry day on Open Farm Sunday and we enjoyed a walk around the farm with about 20 visitors. We then had tea and biscuits in the barn. Crucial to the walk was my illustration of the three-tier sheep system that explained how the mountain flocks of upland Britain are a vital part of the whole of the UK's flock of sheep. This is because the older mountain ewes are crossed to a Bluefaced Leicester to produce a mule sheep – the ultimate milky mother. The mule is then crossed to a meat-producing sheep known as a 'terminal sire' such as a Texel. The resulting lamb stocks the supermarket shelves of the UK. Without the purebred mountain flocks the whole system would collapse and the health of the whole flock of UK sheep would be compromised without the hardiness of the hills.

It feels like an on-going battle for support for upland farms, but we must take up arms and fight for government support. Our strengths are biodiversity on our high nature value farms, and the way that farmers maintain the landscape that millions of visitors a year love, along with the quality food products that we produce.

Also this week I was given the opportunity to explain my love of upland farming on the 'Rock and Roll Farming Podcast' with Will Evans. Hopefully my love for the uplands and my animals was clear in the broadcast. I feel it is important to take every opportunity to explain to the public why upland farmers are not the enemy.

We had some good news in early June that Hector had managed to secure an allotment in Borrowdale where we could summer our cows. The allotment was owned by a neighbour, and is in the Lake District National Park. Traditionally our farm had a lot of land in the Borrowdale Valley but it was sold off as a separate lot at auction, so it was nice to be offered some 'back'. It was a beautiful area of bio diverse wood pasture, about 135 acres, and ideal for our native breed cows.

In order to make best use of the allotment Hector bought six more Aberdeen Angus heifers. They were bought over the internet and transported here by the owner. They were good healthy cows and seamlessly joined the herd. I suppose that the videos and pictures sent over the internet were doing the job the cattle dealer previously did in moving animals around the country. Our farm was a temporary stopping off point for drovers as they brought stock from Scotland to England historically.

Other new arrivals on the farm were three Muscovy ducks that Hector asked for for his birthday, and two silkie hens that I bought myself to glamourize the garden alongside the ex-battery hens. They did not glamourize the garden for long, as within a week they had vanished without trace.

After I had taken my youngest son to school for his last GCSE exam, the last school run after nineteen years, Antony and I decided to go away for a break. Where does a farming officer and a sustainable energy consultant go for a holiday? As both of us were concerned with reducing carbon usage in our jobs we decided to go on a train journey rather than by aeroplane.

I had recently seen a newspaper article about a wild-flower festival in the Bohinj Valley in Slovenia. It was about 20 years since we had been to the Bohinj valley, and we had both remembered how spectacularly beautiful it was there.

Antony set about seeing if we could get there and back by train for the week that he had without any work commitments. It was possible to get the train from Oxenholme, Kendal to Bohinjska Bistrica around 48 hours later. The journey would be broken in Munich; we would have five days in Bohinj, before travelling back on the train, breaking the journey in Brussels.

Rucksacks were packed and off we went to see the hay

meadows of Bohinj. We arrived in the middle of a heat wave. The valley looked absolutely stunning. On the first day we took a cable car up Vogel Mountain and then walked to the summit of Sija at 1800m. For the remaining time we walked around the valley bottoms, about 20 miles per day, visiting alpine pastures and museums about alpine farming.

It seemed that the people of Bohinj, and the Triglav National Park, had a real pride in their farming which was always described as their 'cultural heritage'. We were given some lovely brochures that said that the people of the area apologised if they didn't stop to chat, but they were busy with their cows. There were information boards in several locations about farming, and the meadows themselves took your breath away. I counted so many different species of orchid and lily; there were wild Sweet Williams and a whole host of other flowers. The whole valley was an advert for nature friendly farming.

It gradually began to dawn on me that whilst the valley had been left in picture perfect condition with alpine huts and flower meadows, there were not any actual farmers left working traditionally in the valley. The alpine huts were either empty or occupied with holidaymakers. In June the cows from the Bohinj Valley should have been grazing the alpine meadows, but there were no animals or farmers to be seen.

It was a beautiful holiday destination made perfect by the meadows that were no longer eaten by cows but cut and wrapped in plastic into big bales of silage, for whom I did not find out, but traditional farming was essentially dead.

It was an interesting illustration of a farmed environment in a National Park, but without any remaining farmers. In the Lake District National Park we have fewer farmers than previously, and they are regularly criticised for not farming alongside nature closely enough, but at least we still have our indigenous farming families so crucial to our cultural heritage. Once back home I was inspired by the meadows, but determined that our National Park must be peopled. It cannot become a museum, however beautiful that museum may be. It was also a good illustration of why the Lake District and the Yorkshire Dales are special, as the last mention of shared alpine grazing that I could find in Bohinj was in the 1970s. Their culture of shared grazing had been lost within my lifetime. Ours must not be.

When we returned home there was little time for reflection because silaging was underway. Unlike the previous year it had not been hot and dry enough to make hay, so this year we had to make silage instead.

This is when the grass is 'pickled' in plastic. It is such a life saver that we have now got the ability to make silage, unlike the hill farmer before the 1970s whose survival and existence for the following year depended on the ability to make hay for the animals to eat during the winter. A wet summer could have been a very stressful time indeed.

The meadows were cut, scaled out, rowed up, baled and wrapped in plastic and stacked ready for winter. We had our winter feed, but it was disappointing that we had to use plastic to preserve it, especially single use plastic.

If the summers continue to be like this we will have to look at using the silage clamp again rather than wrapping everything in plastic. The clamp is an area at the back of the cowshed where the grass can be stored and covered over. We have not used the clamp to date as we do not have a 'grab' to take the silage out of the clamp, and machinery is expensive. Every passing season throws up new issues, and new questions about the sustainability of the farm.

After silaging we had shearing. This year Hector did the shearing without my help, as I was working. It was a long, hard job and he was glad when it was over. Once it was over we could begin to think about putting the cows onto the allotment at Borrowdale. Our neighbours have an environmental agreement that requires them to graze with cows, so it seems ideal that our cows can help them with this extensive grazing as they do not have any cows of their own.

Borrowdale is apparently the longest uninhabited stretch of valley in England. It has one farmhouse, and one derelict farmhouse, and is otherwise grazed extensively for the benefit of the rare plants that grow there. Part of the valley is owned by the Cavendish family from Holker Hall, and the remainder by the Friends of the Lake District. To avoid confusion with its more famous namesake, Borrowdale in the northern lakes, it is usually referred to as Westmorland Borrowdale.

Borrowdale is largely deserted but it is not without controversy. It was once suggested as a site for a reservoir, 27 wind turbines were another proposition by the Bretherdale Commoners, and it was once proposed as a holiday destination. A Manchester based company called Natural Retreats wanted to build ten timber framed holiday homes in the valley. The project proposed would have cost six million pounds to construct, but was not supported by Eden District Council and never took place.

Borrowdale was described by the walking guide author Alfred Wainwright as 'the most beautiful valley outside of the Lake District', but since the boundary extension on 2016 is it now part of the park. As we walked our cows along the lane from Low Borrowbridge to Borrowdale we were walking out of one national park and into another. We were now farming in two national parks. There can't be many farmers who can say that!

The cows enjoyed their 'natural retreat' in the valley for the summer. They appeared to be trampling some of the bracken down, and the displays of orchids on the hillsides were quite breath taking.

There was also an abundance of dragonflies and mayflies buzzing about in the valley. While walking up the steep hillsides looking for the cows it could be quite difficult to avoid stepping on them. The cows could be quite tricky to find, so all in all we spent quite a lot of time walking and driving on the quad around this beautiful, deserted valley.

We were also preparing for an influx of visitors. One of the ways in which we were trying to generate more income was by holding events. At the beginning of July we were going to hold the Saunders Lakeland Mountain Marathon. This is a two day navigational challenge. The event was going to start and finish on our farm, and have around 1,500 competitors. The event is run on a not for profit basis, and donates around £9,000 each year to local charities such as the Calvert Trust, Bendrigg Trust and the North West Air Ambulance. At the end of June portable toilets for the event were delivered, and stood like sentry guards along the edge of the Roman fort. Shame the Roman latrines were not still functional; it would have saved a lot of money on portable toilet hire.

Holiday

It is absolutely perfect
I am standing
Knee deep in flowers
Sweet Williams and lilies
Growing wild.

The Alpine huts
Flower meadows
Pollinators
Wooded valleys
Perfection.

"Looking at this"
You say
"Is there not an argument
For saying that sheep
Have wrecked the Lake District?"

As we understand
More, over the next few days
We realise
That these valleys
Are essentially dead.

They are all illustrations
Of conservation
But not of farming
No one farms here now
All the families have left.

They work in towns
And come back at
Weekends to enjoy
The view.
They do not farm.

Whilst it is
Alive with nature
In human terms
This valley is
Dead.

We must not allow
Our Cumbrian valleys
To die a death.
We must farm on quietly
Through the political noise.

When there is quiet
When the noise of
Dissent has abated
Maybe then they will
Appreciate the farmers

Who keep on keeping on
Through Brexit
Through climate emergencies
Through disease outbreaks
Throughout life.

July

At the beginning of July the farm was waiting for an influx of fell running visitors, sitting pretty in the sunshine, the grass greening up nicely after being cut, ready for the visitors. In the rough pastures that were not cut for silage there was an abundance of wild flowers. After the pink orchids came a wave of white orchids, accompanied by flowers such as meadow vetchling, red clover, betony and geraniums.

Borrowdale is famous for its wild flowers and the neighbouring valley of Bretherdale is supposed to be equally spectacular. We had never been to Bretherdale before, so one sunny Sunday we decided to walk and see the meadows there in bloom.

Bretherdale is a remarkable valley in more ways than one. Its exclusion from the Lake District national Park until 2016 has left it undeveloped. Property has obviously not been of value, and in the first half an hour of walking through Bretherdale we passed several derelict farmhouses. Bretherdale means 'valley of the brothers' and you cannot help but think about all the families who must have lived here years ago. This quiet valley must have been alive with people going about their farming business. It is a real contrast to the valleys of the central Lake District where it is very unusual to see any property uninhabited – if only by visitors and not locals. Even in the Lake District, in July, there are very quiet places still to be found if you seek them out.

As we walked through Greenholme we passed a deserted farmhouse. Interestingly this had a For Sale sign on it. When I enquired at the estate agents, it was a grade 2 listed farmhouse, dilapidated, with buildings and around 60 acres of land. The guide price was £90,000. There was no one interested in buying it. We are quite busy at this time of year, and I do not get back to the estate agent for three weeks, by which time there are several people interested in buying it, and so it was to be sold by auction.

Had we acted quicker, we may have been able to buy it for £90,000. Too late was the cry. I went to the auction and watched it sell for over £300,000. Lesson learnt. Act more quickly.

There were plenty of jobs to occupy us during July. The remainder of the sheep down at Low Park Farm needed to be sheared. The lambs needed to be vaccinated, given a mineral bolus and wormed. The wool was squashed into big bags called 'wool sheets' and then sold directly to a buyer. This got us about three times the amount that we would have got from the British Wool Board. Some wool was kept on one side to make into knitting wool.

I attended the Lakeland Book of the Year awards and was given a runner up certificate. Hunter Davis the author described *Lakelanders* as 'rather a strange tale' so I didn't know what to make of that!

The Saunders Lakeland Mountain Marathon was a very successful event. It was fun to see all the marquees set up on the hay meadows. In order to apologise for any inconvenience to our neighbours they were all invited for a meal

and a drink in the refreshments marquee on the Friday night before the event. At midnight the event organisers had to ask the local farmers to leave as the competitors were trying to get to sleep! The event went off without any major incidents, and thankfully everybody seemed to enjoy it. The river was a popular destination once the competitors had finished running.

Towards the middle of July the hedgerows and parts of the farm turned purple as the melancholy thistle, knapweed and great burnet started to flower. The old vegetable garden where the Muscovy ducks were living was a mass of pink roses, tumbling over the walls and the roof of the pigsty.

Sadly we found several squashed hedgehogs on the road outside the house, and after the fourth I wrote to the parish council to ask if they could possibly supply some hedgehog signs. No reply. It wasn't a random request, I had seen on the news that they were available. Hector also disturbed some noisy hedgehogs mating in the vegetable garden one night when he went to shut the ducks in, so there were still some around thank goodness.

On the 23 July we decided to wean the lambs from their mums. The ewes had begun to look very thin and tired, and the lambs no longer needed the milk. Some Texel lambs were big enough to be sold straight away at auction, and the rest were put down to Low Park to spend the rest of the summer growing there.

Something rather unexpected happened in that I exhibited some photographs in an art gallery exhibition. It was an exhibition called 'Shepherds of Instagram' that aimed to show some images of sheep taken by shepherds to bridge the gap between farmers and consumers. I never got to see the exhibition at Keswick Museum but it was very well received.

On the last day of July Moss the border collie had a lovely litter of puppies. This would be her third and final litter. She nestled herself comfortably in the sheep shed in the straw, and lovingly fed her puppies diligently. She was an example to us all of love and dedication. She didn't like to spend more than five minutes away from them at first, but I knew that in eight weeks time she would be ready for a rest when the puppies were old enough to go to new homes. Before that they had a lot of growing to do, and a lot of learning to do, as did we all.

Social Capital

It is a wet day
At Grayrigg Show
Mud up to my knees
Rain down my neck

"What possible good
What 'social capital'
Can possibly come
From a field full of mud?"

Watching the sheep
Chatting to farmers
Huddled under umbrellas
With hoods and hats dripping

There is nowhere
To sit, so in the afternoon
I go into the auction mart's
Trailer for tea and a scone

We chat about
Business sustainability
Farm futures and viability
Supply chain vulnerability

Then I am asked
To go with the auction directors
To meet the chief economist
Of the Bank of England

Yes, no good can ever come
Of standing around
In wet waterproofs
In muddy fields.

August

Throughout August the cows were very elusive. They enjoyed roaming free in Borrowdale, and it often took us hours to find them. They were living a very happy 'free range' lifestyle.

I was also quite elusive at home as there were so many shows and shepherds meets to attend. There is a flurry of activity in the summer as shepherds show off their best sheep at local shows before the autumn sales. The shepherds meets were traditionally a time for returning lost sheep and exchanging tups. Today tups are generally sold and not exchanged, so the shows act as a shop window before the autumn sales.

My job for the Lake District National Park at shows was to build up a relationship with the shepherds, and feed back any queries into the Lake District National Park Authority or partner organisations. It was also to interact with the public who visited the shows. To assist with that we made two cards to hand out at the shows, one saying why the National Park was supporting farming (I had had members of the public asking me this at Greenholme Show) and a second card to engage people with the sheep show by showing what the judge is looking for in a good show sheep.

The second card acted as an excellent way to get people to approach the sheep pens and look closely at the sheep. We also had the card made into a large banner to put onto

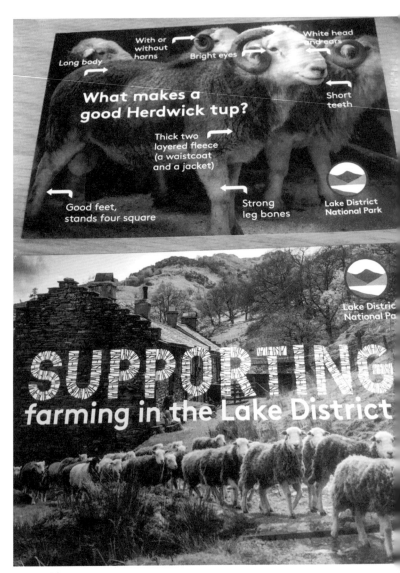

the sheep pens at shows.

They were very long days, often wet, and farm work had to be done before driving to the shepherds meets, but it was very rewarding. People really appreciated the opportunity to chat about farming. An academic from an Australian university who was visiting the UK asked to talk to me and asked how did I know that I was fully integrated and accepted by the farming community. I could think of no better way to answer than to suggest that she came to a shepherds meet with me.

When the first sheep class was called at the show someone shouted, "Where's Andrea? Can you hold my baby?" The academic turned to me and said, "Ok, I believe you. You are accepted by this community." I was already part of the shepherding community before I started the job. I had shown sheep and spent a lot of time chatting to other farmers at shows and events. My concerns as a farmer were the same as the other farmers' concerns, so there was no issue with 'fitting in' or being accepted. It was also accepted by everyone that money needed to be made off farm, and most families had people working off farm in order to support the farm, so it was not a big issue.

It was not really a question of 'poacher turned gamekeeper' as the National Park did not really have a bad reputation with farmers. It didn't really have much of a reputation with farmers that I knew, good or bad. The authority was determined to build these relationships in order to include more about the future of farming in its management plan, following on from the Park being inscribed as a World Heritage Site with the cultural heritage of shepherding one of its key assets. I think that farmers could see that the authority genuinely wanted to engage with farmers. As I kept saying to people – would I be working for the National Park if I didn't believe that they supported farming? No – and they have given me no reason not to believe that they genuinely do support farming.

The puppies continued to grow and thrive, and there were some new arrivals in the vegetable garden as well. One of the Muscovy ducks sat on a clutch of eggs and hatched them. We moved her into the old pigsty while they were tiny, and then back into the garden. All the ducks took collective responsibility for the new arrivals. When they went out of the garden for a drink it was a group operation. The two ducks went at the front, followed by a line of ducklings, with Sir Francis Drake bringing up the rear. They all took their responsibility to keep the ducklings safe very seriously. It was great to see them waddling across the yard.

August was also a time of great activity on the farm as we had contractors fencing off our riparian strips around the farm. These are riverside strips of land that were to exclude grazing and naturally regenerate, to make the riverbanks more resilient in serious flood events, allow more habitats for wildlife, and keep the river cool for fishes. It was great to actually get on with the work as it had taken so long to get the application approved. Things were moving forwards, slowly but surely.

August 2019 seemed to be characterised by extreme weather. One day, such as Grayrigg Show day, it could be absolutely pouring down all day and we would be standing in awful sloppy deep mud around the sheep pens, whereas two days later at Kentmere Show it was so hot that I had to go and lie down in the shade for a bit. We seemed to lurch from one extreme to another. It is very difficult to plan events when the weather is as unpredictable as this. On wet days at shows it was so disappointing for the show organisers – they would attract few visitors paying gate money, and the day was not nearly as enjoyable for those taking part. Often there is talk of moving show dates, but there is no time in the Lake District where good weather is guaranteed. May and September are generally good months, but realistically anything can happen at any time weather wise.

Best Coat

"Surely this yow
Has the best coat?"
I ask, observing
The sheep in the pens

Back to the wind
Hair escaping from hat
Mittens over gloves
And three pairs of socks on

"If you think she's
The best, you show her."
Is the answer, and I heave
The sheep out of the pen

It's quite a physical feat
To stand there with a jumpy yow
While the judge lights another fag
And contemplates the line up

Positions are changed
Opinions discussed
The nearer you are to the left
The more likely to win a ticket

4th. No rosette this time
"It likely had the best FLEECE
But not the best COAT"
I'm told. Reality dawns

Of course.
Best coat for the sheep
Not fleece for the spinner
I live and learn.

September

September is usually a good month weather wise, and a lot of the visitors to Cumbria have gone home, leaving the locals to enjoy the events this month.

Unfortunately in 2019 the Westmorland Show was a total washout. It was the first time since 2012 that I had not exhibited sheep at the show, but this year I was very busy as the Lake District National Park Authority were sponsoring the Swaledale Sheep classes. There were few spectators as it was relentlessly wet all morning. It was such a shame for the organisers. By the early afternoon a lot of people had started to make their way through the mud home.

We had decided upon a world heritage theme for our Lake District National Park Authority stand, and we had a variety of farm products made within the UNESCO World Heritage site on display. We also had bread made locally to give away, and coffee from another World Heritage site. A lot of time had been taken in deciding how to display the products to best effect, and it was very sad that in the afternoon there were few visitors to our tent.

At home my parents plans to concert the old taproom from the coaching inn into their home were continuing apace. We had to put in a new septic tank system as the old one did not meet new regulations designed to safeguard water quality. Unfortunately the old septic tank was located

inside the area of the Scheduled Ancient Monument, so the new system had to be monitored archaeologically.

As I studied archaeology at university I could do this myself, so spent a day cautiously looking down into a hole as the old tank was removed and the replacement put in. Thankfully the replacement system fitted into the hole left by the previous tank, so no extra disturbance to the ground was required, and no Roman artefacts were discovered!

We had two days in the house without water while this work was undertaken. We had a portaloo in the yard, but for one night I went to stay at Tebay Services Hotel so that I could have a bath. The room was a 'crafted' room with tweed curtains, headboard, throws and cushions made from local wool. I thoroughly enjoyed it.

I needed to further investigate diversification options for the farm. With the possibility of leaving Europe looking more an more certain, there would be a subsequent loss of the Basic Payment Scheme for farm support so we had to look for an alternative source of income once my temporary job at the national park had ended. My friend and I decided to look at how other people were marketing their Roman sites, so we spent three days travelling the length of Hadrian's Wall visiting all the sites along the way. We did a seven mile walk along the wall at Sycamore Gap in hail, wind and rain. I think it started snowing at one point, but we thoroughly enjoyed it. We could see that even with few remains visible over ground it was possible to make a viable visitor attraction by using information boards and audio visual displays in visitor centres.

It was definitely a possibility for the future. I had to look seriously at all diversification opportunities and decide which looked like the best option. Back at home we were busy with more work for our Countryside Stewardship agreement. We had asked for permission to include owl boxes, not actually allowed near a motorway or railway line, but we knew that we had owls living on site. We had been allowed the funding for the owl boxes so set about building them following the instructions on a video from the Barn Owl Trust. The boxes were put up in some trees near the house and in the hay barn. We would have to wait to see if anyone moved in – preferably an owl!

September is always a great month for fungus and this year was no exception. We found many different kinds of wax caps. These are small fungi and are usually found in unimproved grasslands, so it was great to see them. Whilst visiting Matterdale Common I found a whole mini village of fly agaric toadstools. I could imagine Beatrix Potter would have been in her element sketching them.

The puppies were growing well and soon it would be time for them to go to their new homes. I would be sad to see them go as they would be the last of Moss' offspring, but she was ready to see them off – spending longer away from them and not so anxious about returning to them. She seemed to know when it was time for them to go and began sleeping separately from them. When the time came for them to go Moss went happily back to sleeping in her own kennel in the old milking parlour instead of sleeping in the sheep shed. Job done. The seasons roll on.

Valuable Time

I have always wanted
A grandfather clock
To stand in the hall
Marking the passing hours

Surely our farmhouse
Would have had
Such a clock ticking
Chiming the hours

One Saturday morning
At the auction
There is a clock
Made in Penrith 1700

A local clock
Of the right period
For the house
Bid for and bought

How much did
This treasure cost?
Seventy Five pounds
For a much loved clock.

VALUABLE TIME

I say much loved
As sellotaped inside
Is a list of owners
Since 1700

This clock was
An inheritance
Passed from one generation
To the next

The names of farmers
And their farmhouses
Listed out
Only one other female owner

I unpack the clock
From the sheep trailer
My son and I lift
The long case in

Treasured history
Family heirloom
Bought at auction
For the price of a sheep

The things we value
Have changed in recent times
Change is coming quickly
Even in Westmorland

October

In early October you could smell autumn was in the air. Change comes quickly to the valley. One day it seems to be late summer and the next day autumn. Trees lose their leaves very quickly, usually within a week, unlike in low-land areas where the process is much more prolonged. One very windy day and most of the leaves have gone. Autumn was here, and preparations must be made for winter.

The first big job was to walk the cows home from Bor-rowdale. They were thankfully used to following us to new grazing, and understand that is where they are going so do not object to following us. As we got nearer to home they started walking faster and faster and then broke into a run when they saw the house. They know where they are going and were happy to come into the barn. We had two areas with cubicles ready for them, with areas to put out the si-lage in between. We have room for 30 cows on each side, but we do not have anywhere near that number.

The cows had to be sorted so that cows went one way onto one side of the building, and the calves went the other way and are weaned. The cows needed a rest now from the exertion of feeding and looking after their calves. They could still see each other, but they could not get to their mother's milk. The calves were growing at a tremendous rate, and the health of the cows would suffer if they fed them for much longer.

The novelty of the situation, the calves being inside on fresh straw, seemed to distract somewhat from the stress of the separation from their mothers. There was remarkably little calling out, and the cows settled into life in the barns. They were fed on big bales of silage that we had made earlier in the summer. The reason for them being inside was so that they did not 'poach' the grass at this time of year – turn the turf to mud – which they would do if they were allowed to stay outside. They are perfectly happy outside, it is just damaging to the land.

Grass to eat is in short supply at this time of year. The lambs were separated into those being sold for meat, and those being sold for flock replacements. The flock replacements stayed down at Low Park, and those that were going to be sold for meat came inside and were weighed. Those ready to be sold were sold immediately, and those that needed to be fattened were kept inside and fed on silage and sheep 'nuts'. These 'nuts' are bought in feed. We would rather not feed commercial food, as this increases the carbon footprint of the farm, and is not a sustainable practice, but needs must and we have limited choices. If we fattened the sheep outside on grass they would not be ready until they were over a year old and therefore 'hogget' and not lamb. It would take more than eighteen months for them to fatten on grass, by which time they would be virtually unsaleable in today's markets.

In the future something must change. We will find a way to sell our hogget that has been fattened on grass, or we will make our own product to sell. For this year, we must continue to feed bought in food. It is not ideal and a lot of hill farmers are in a similar situation. If there was a good price for 'store' lambs and we could sell them directly at weaning to a farm with better grass that would be ideal. This is the way that hill farms have operated in the recent past, but Brexit and the market conditions have meant that the store lamb price is generally below the cost of production. It is important that we are financially as well as environmentally sustainable.

The smaller Ouessant lambs also came inside. They can struggle outside during their first winter, so we tend to bring them in if the weather is wet. There were still shows and shepherds meets to attend in October. These later shows are largely just local shepherds without visitors. It is a chance for everybody to meet up and there is always a sit down dinner in a pub involved (we eat our dinner at dinnertime here in Cumbria, and by that I mean in the middle of the day. Breakfast, dinner and tea.) The autumn sales of sheep had started and I attended a lot of them as a sponsor, giving out information from DEFRA to farmers about what might happen when we leave the European Union.

Rural crime is often a topic of discussion when farmers get together and we had a bizarre experience of our own to talk about in October. A car came into the yard at 3.15am on a Saturday night. It drove several times up and down

A muddy day for Buttermere Show.

the lane very slowly and noisily (we later found out that the driver had hit the bank further down the lane and had a flat tyre). It then came back into the yard and Antony went downstairs. The driver of the car asked if he could borrow some tools. At 3.30am!! Antony said no and he was going to call the police. The man said he was lost travelling from Bury to Newcastle.

He then got into the car and drove off very fast down the lane towards the Howgill Fells. I was really worried about him driving at top speed down there, and Antony phoned the police to explain what had happened. The police arrived and followed him down the lane. They later came back and told us that the man had driven into Carlingill (a stream in a very steep sided valley) and they had to rescue him and the car. He was unhurt. A breakdown truck arrived but it could not fit down the lane. There was then a lot of lights flashing and activity. The police said that they arrested the man on multiple offences, and that the driver had been 'on the ratch' (looking about for things to steal). Some neighbours had a quad bike stolen the following night. Rural crime is a threat to all of our property, and to our sanity.

At the end of the month I went on a three-day visit to the North York Moors National Park, to look at the work that their farming officers do there. It was very interesting to see projects that they had been involved in. In particular it was interesting to see how wet, boggy fields in valley bottoms were valued as important wildlife sites. We have any amount of wet, boggy fields in Cumbria!

It was great hospitality from the North Your Moors National Park and it is always a good thing to put your own assets into perspective. One of our greatest assets in the Lake Distract National Park is all the hard working, knowledgeable farmers. At the end of October it was time for Buttermere Shepherds Meet. The field was unbelievably muddy, but what an illustration it was of the dedication of the profession. The show must go on, and on it went.

The Price of Wool

"The price of wool
Has fallen through the floor
So don't bother selling it
Keep it for another year

Wrap it well
And store it somewhere dry
Maybe the price
Will be better next year

If we buy it this year
The quote is negative
Meaning you pay us
To take it away

The price of wool
Has just dropped you see
There's nothing we can do
There's no point in selling it now."

And yet this world and
The next generation are all about
Sustainability, low carbon lifestyles
Cutting back on waste, recycling more

Wool is the ultimate
Sustainable product
It grows, captures carbon,
And has to be harvested

It's biodegradable
Washable, waterproof,
Windproof, carbon positive
And most of all cheap

But there is no market for wool
So it sits in the barn
Waiting for someone
To wake up to wool.

Editor's Note: Wool is also the best thing ever to wear –
Kendal's motto 'Wool is my Bread' will return one day soon.
(obvioiusly this can be delet4ed!

November

On the first day of November we travelled to Skipton to buy a working dog. We had watched some videos before the auction, but basically you had three minutes to watch a dog before bidding. It is a very difficult way to buy a dog, as you have no information about its temperament with people or other dogs – only with sheep. It was quite a nerve-wracking experience.

Hector bought a fully trained dog called Keyva. We had seen her work sheep, but everything else about her was unknown. It was rather a difficult purchase and I think we both felt a bit nervous about it. Keyva was very quiet in the car on the way home – at least she did not seem overly aggressive.

The last shepherds meets of the year took place at Walna Scar in the Duddon Valley and Stoneside in Eskdale. These were small, friendly, locals-only events with hot dinners and usually singing in the pub afterwards. At Walna Scar some collectors of traditional folk songs came to listen to the singing, I don't know if they found anything especially unusual.

At these last shepherds meets there were many classes for pairs and groups of sheep. I made myself useful by holding sheep for people who had more than one sheep in a class, and really enjoyed showing Herdwick Sheep. I may have been there as an officer of the Lake District

National Park, but I felt truly part of the event.

We had to have a Tb test that we had not expected. Thankfully the cows were all inside so there was no issue about getting them in. We also had the cows pregnancy tested while the vet was here. Thankfully we were Tb free, but rather shockingly seven out of our 22 cows were not pregnant. This was not what we had expected and was very disappointing. The cows had had a lovely summer free ranging in the Borrowdale Valley, but the vegetation there must have been lacking something and they were not able to get pregnant.

Shepherds meet.

This would have implications for future farm management and for the cows themselves. The cows would have to be sold if they were not pregnant, as we could not afford to keep them for another year if they did not produce a calf. Going further, we would have to re-evaluate our plans. It seemed that we could not have a high quality suckler herd, and do conservation grazing in Borrowdale. It seemed as if the way forward would be to rear more 'bucket calves' from dairy cows, and not breed from them. This was rather disappointing as Hector had wanted to build up a suckler herd, but we could not do both. This is the kind of thing that you can only learn through experience, and is what makes farming so fascinating. A farm is a big puzzle to be solved. If you move one piece of the jigsaw the other bits often do not fit neatly back into place.

If you talk to people with an interest in agri-environmental agreements they will tell you that cows can get all the nutrition that they need from wood pasture, indeed it is currently in vogue to suggest that large areas of common land that have been used for centuries for grazing hefted herds of sheep should be 'reverted' back to wood pasture and cows should be used to graze the uplands of Cumbria rather than sheep. I have nothing against grazing existing wood pasture with cows, but I do believe that historically sheep would also have been allowed to graze in wood pasture. As for running a suckler herd in such an area – our experience tells us that despite giving them a mineral bolus the nutritional value of the food they were eating was not enough to get them in calf. The same cows had all got pregnant on the in-bye grassland last year. It had been a valuable learning experience.

As for the suggestion that large areas of upland common could be cleared of sheep in order to 'create wood pasture where it was once present' I would question this. Firstly because wood pasture was not 'once present' in a lot of locations (this is the justification used for making this environmental change). In her book *Upland Agriculture and the Environment* professor Lois Mansfield explains that by using pollen analysis it is possible to conclude that 'large areas of the Lake District were montane treeless environments well before the influx of larger populations around 5000BP'(Before Present – that is 7,000 years ago). It is a misunderstanding to believe that all the fell tops, the open commons that are part of the agro-pastoral cultural environment of Cumbria, were once wooded.

My main objection to the idea of removing sheep in favour of 'a return to wood pasture' is that the hefted flocks themselves are a cultural asset of critical importance to the uplands of Cumbria. The designation of the Lake District as a World Heritage Site by UNESCO in 2016 was largely because of the agro pastoral cultural heritage of shepherding.

Without these hefted flocks we lose the 'cultural capital' of Cumbria. The breeds themselves are also a unique genetic resource specifically adapted to our area that we would be foolish to lose. The most important asset that Cumbria has, to me, are the hefted flocks of sheep. If we lose them we will lose our cultural events and a richness of knowledge and understanding that the shepherds have built up over generations. Put bluntly, if we lose our sheep, we lose our own identity.

At the beginning of November we were thinking about our own sheep. Two 'teaser tups' called Robert and Jeffrey that Hector had bought went in with the yows. These were vasectomised rams, and they must have thought that all their Christmases had come at once to have first pick of all the ladies. We were using these tups this year as now that I had a job off farm we had limited time in which to work together at lambing time. I had up to 17 days that I could take as annual leave, so we wanted as many sheep to lamb in the first 17-day cycle as possible.

This year we were keeping fewer sheep 'pure' and only breeding flock replacements from what we considered to be our best, fittest ewes. These were chosen by observation, and by seeing which ewes were at the front of the group as we walked them the three and a half miles home from Low Park into the meadows where they would meet the tups. Any who dawdled did not get put to the pure bred Welsh Speckle or Rough Fell tups, instead they were crossed to the Texel to produce a meaty lamb. Hopefully this policy, along with regular body condition scoring the ewes, checking that they had the right amount of weight on and adjusting their feed requirements if necessary, along with close observation of the ewes will improve our flock in time.

We put a harness with a 'crayon' onto the tups, and the teasers seemed to have done their job as the sheep were quickly marked on their bottoms indicating that they had been tupped. The proof of the pudding would come in April, but it looked like the strategy had worked.

After having had a couple more days out in the Yorkshire Dales, I decided to put in planning permission for two shepherds huts to run as holiday lets. It seemed that this would be the best option for diversification. I was also working on a woodland management plan, which had to be completed in order to put in an application for a Higher Tier woodland grant to fence off some of the woodland to allow the natural regeneration of trees. I was also applying for a farm diversification grant. It seemed as if there was so much paperwork to do that it was following me around, stacked up on top of my head, weighing me down. Upland farmers have to be Jack or Jill of all trades, and hopefully master of at least one.

Tree Guards

Roman soldiers used to line this gorge
Seeing off invaders from the north
Then border raiders came, then
Gunpowder, cannonballs found in molehills still today.

Now an army of tree guards and fence posts
Slowly march across the fell
Planted with military precision
Guarding and claiming the landscape for their own

The previous farmer here always sat in the same chair
Watching his hefted flock from the kitchen table
Now we watch the army of plastic tree guards
That are commandeering the landscape

Scrub. Not trees but scrub
These bushes will increase wildlife
And make the landscape more resilient to flooding
But it just doesn't feel right to me

There was no regard for the hefted flocks
Their loss is grieved by the older farmers in the valley
They tell me about how they got to their heft
Under a railway bridge, wistfully pointing to the fell

I feel as if something is amiss
There was no consideration for our cultural heritage
There is only matted grass
And the memory of a sheep flock.

We have no memory of that sheep flock
But we still have the same kitchen chair
Looking out at the same fell view
And it's not quite right to me.

There is too much change.
There is too little compromise
The problem is not the addition of trees
It's the total removal of sheep and culture

The fell feels bereaved
It is lacking in something
Meanwhile the tree guards march on
Occupying more and more of my view.

I feel I should apologize for my opinion
I do genuinely want to see more trees
Just not to the exclusion
Of what really matters here.

"The old boys that used to live here
They'd be horrified, horrified to see this"
I daren't say to my neighbour that I
Am quite horrified myself.

Time will tell
The scrub will grow
The hefted sheep will become
Just a memory of a memory.

December

December came quietly and brought a little dusting of snow to the Howgill Fells. There was no heavy snowfall this year, and very few frosty mornings. Winter routines continued, with feeding ewes and walking dogs in the short daylight hours. Christmas was a welcome diversion and time to see our family.

The end of the year brought a time of reflection. We had been at Low Borrowbridge Farm for nearly two years, and we were well on the way to building the sustainable farm that we dreamed of, but what actually is that elusive thing – a 'sustainable farm'?

My job at the Lake District National Park had made me question this more than ever as I had been discussing with colleagues about the implications if we are to deliver nature recovery, adapt to climate change and secure the future of farming in the uplands. At work we had a Venn diagram with these three concerns as the circles, but what actually was the elusive 'bit in the middle', the intersection, the 'Reuleaux triangle' to give it its proper term? What could we do on our own farm to make our business truly sustainable – and how did this relate to the key challenges that we were facing?

Low Borrowbridge Farm

What actually did we mean when we said that we wanted a sustainable farm? It is a farm that:

- Lives within its means environmentally. It does not have to import animal feed, the environment here sustains the animals.

- Lives within its means economically. It does not make a loss. It provides work for our family and helps to sustain us economically.

- It contributes quality genetics to the sheep breeds that we keep. It helps to sustain our native breeds.

- It respects and enhances the cultural heritage of the area (and promotes this to a global audience).

- It is carbon neutral or sequesters carbon.

- It provides habitats for the wild animals and plants that are native to this area to support them (and provides new networks for them to travel about in safety).

- It mitigates climate change and adapts to protect the environment here.

- It produces high quality food.

- It protects, and where possible restores, the historic environment.

Being a sustainable farm is always going to be a work in progress, as things are constantly changing – be that government policy or weather patterns or a whole host of other variables. How are we doing after a total of ten years farming with my family?

Environmentally sustainable

Our understanding of the flora and fauna of our farm has increased as we have come to know our new farm. It will take several years to fully understand the habitats here, particularly in the woodlands, as we have never owned woodlands before. It was a steep learning curve to write our woodland management plan.

We have red squirrels, otters, deer, hares and salmon amongst other wildlife. We have an abundance of butterflies including the rare pearl-bordered fritillary. We have a variety of rare trees and plants including wych elm trees that have survived Dutch elm disease, and mature oak trees. Plants are a variety of woodland plants including spignel, with alpine plants amongst the rough grazing. We also have haymeadow plants in the rough grazing, mature hedgerows, mosses, ferns and lichen.

In order to keep all these on the farm we have designated some areas as wildlife areas that will not be grazed, established riparian strips that will stabilise riverbanks, provide habitats and cool the river. We have laid hedgerows traditionally to benefit nesting birds, and will shortly fence the woodlands to exclude grazing animals so that they can naturally regenerate.

We have taken some wood for fuel from the woodlands and will continue to do this in order to make ourselves sustainable in terms of energy usage. We will hopefully get a biomass boiler and burn only our own wood.

We will continue to rotationally graze and improve our soils, and more areas will soon be able to be grazed in this way once our riparian strips are fenced off. Moving the animals about regularly ensures that more of the root structure of the grass is retained beneath the soil, and there is less run off in heavy rainfall or flooding. If the climate behaves as it is predicted to due to global warming and climate change, there will be more of these serious rainfall events in summer and winter in the future. Our land will be better prepared to meet the challenge of climate change.

The riparian strips will form a three and a half mile long nature recovery network allowing wild animals to travel about in safety. This may also become invaluable as the climate changes, as some wild species are expected to migrate north as our country becomes warmer.

Culturally Sustainable

We keep our native breed of sheep, Rough Fell Sheep, and are a member of the Rough Fell Sheep Breed Society. Hector is on the working council of the breed society and we attend all of their events when we can. We support the breed society sales, and have plans to show sheep at local shows in the future. We have not shown many for the last couple of years due to moving farm and my new job, etc.

We are also keeping a high quality flock of Welsh Hill Speckle Faced sheep here in Cumbria, which may be important if, heaven forbid, we have any serious disease outbreaks that mean that the sheep in Snowdonia are lost.

The farm has a successor, my middle son Hector, and the skills he learns whilst working for other farmers and running a hefted fell flock in the Howgills for another family are invaluable. It is such an important part of our farm to know that someone is interested and willing to take it on for the next generation. The farm will also be home to three generations of our family once my parents move in.

The historic environment is protected. The Scheduled Ancient Monument of the Roman fort and complex is safely preserved underground, and the older farm buildings at Low Borrowbridge are in a Countryside Stewardship scheme to ensure that they remain maintained and in use for their original purpose. If possible, more of the cultural landscape at Low Park will be restored in the future.

Financially Sustainable

As I write the farm is just about to stand on its own feet, at 'break even' point. We can see that were conditions to remain as they are at the moment we would be profitable next year. However, there is a great degree of uncertainty as the government are shortly to change from the Basic Payment Scheme and Countryside Stewardship to a new Environmental Land Management Scheme. We do not know how we will fare under this scheme, or how our diversifications will pan out. The financial future is far from certain.

Sustainable in terms of our carbon footprint

There are many different ways to measure the carbon footprint of a farm and there is no agreed methodology for measuring the carbon footprint of an upland farm. In theory, this should easy for our farm to achieve, but it is the most difficult thing to measure.

I have tried three 'carbon farm calculators' to audit the farm, and they have told us that we are sequestering between 0.75 tonnes and 65 tonnes of carbon per annum. This is such a wide variation, that at the moment we are just waiting for an agreed methodology in order to measure the farm. Whether we can then be paid for sequestering carbon remains to be seen, but it does not appear as if it would be a huge amount of money. There has been talk of £25 per tonne of carbon per year sequestered, which would be less than two thousand pounds per year for our farm.

Some of the carbon calculators allow you to see the change in carbon usage if you change the way that you manage your land. I was expecting to see big changes if areas of rough grazing were planted with trees, but there was actually very little difference in the carbon sequestered in the grassland or in the newly planted trees. With this idea it will be wise to wait and see what develops as the methodology for calculating carbon on farms is agreed in the future.

I have never done a calculation that suggest that we are not 'carbon positive', which is probably in contrast to what most of the public would expect about hill farms having seen in the media about how they are very bad for the environment. Being carbon positive means that we create environmental benefits by removing additional carbon dioxide from the air.

Producing quality food

We believe that we are producing quality beef and lamb and we are getting a reasonable price for it in today's market. In order to make this a premium product we need to make it exclusively grass fed, and make a product that we sell. My son is very skilled at knowing when an animal is ready for market, we need to become skilled in providing a consistent supply of grass fed meat in order to produce a product if we wish to get a premium price for our produce.

We are keen to move away from feeding our animals

commercially bought food, be this through feeding them waste from the local brewing industry, turnips that we grow ourselves, or exclusively grass.

We feel that we are doing well with our sheep and that we've 'got the sheep job nearly sorted' and we still need to sort our stocking for our cows or bucket calves. This is a work in progress.

What are our plans for the future?

- Better use of grass on the farm through rotational grazing in order to produce a premium product and improve soils.

- Better habitats for wildlife on the farm as the areas where livestock is excluded develop into nature recovery networks. Possibly plant more trees to extend the woodland areas.

- Continue to improve our flock of sheep. Always work to be done.

- Renovate and insulate our house and install a biomass boiler to use our own wood.

- Restore the cultural environment at Low Park Farm and remain true to our cultural heritage here through the succession process.

- Build a sustainable beef operation, probably through the use of 'bucket calves' which are themselves a by-product of the dairy industry. It is great to provide a home for these calves and add value to them whilst giving them a 'free range' lifestyle on a hill farm.

What is the farm for?

> To produce food?
> To provide habitats for wildlife?
> To make a living?
> To look nice in a National Park setting?

So many questions, but at the end of the day and the end of this book we are just trying to do the right thing. The right thing for the land here, for our family, and for the native breeds of wild animals and farm animals.

Thank you for sharing part of the journey with us. We are well on the road to where we want to be. What does the future hold? The future is based on building a sustainable farm for our family, the community and the environment. Native breeds of animals and people working together, just as they have been on this farm since the sixgteenth century or earlier. The more things change, the more they stay the same.

We have neglected the truth that a good farmer is a craftsman of the highest order, a kind of artist.

Wendell Berry

Afterword

Thank you for reading this book about our second year at Low Borrowbridge Farm. I know that a lot of readers were keen to know how we got on after *Four Seasons* and wanted the story to continue.

As I write in May 2020 I am happy to report that lambing was very successful this year, and very rapid. Those teaser tups certainly did their job. Just as we were beginning to think that we were getting ourselves and our business sorted here, the coronavirus situation came along and threw another spanner in the works for businesses. It remains to see how this crisis will play out, but could it be that local supplies of food and local farmers will be valued after this pandemic? Farmers were named as 'key workers' by the government.

At the end of the book I asked the question "What is the farm for?" I believe that we will be asking this question nationally in the coming months and years as the UK leaves the EU and begins to develop its own policy for agriculture. What are upland farms for? Will their role as producers of high quality food be valued as well as their environmental assets in the new legislation? I think I had better stop writing now as that sounds like a book in itself.

One thing is for sure, the farm provided a wonderful place to live and work during 'lockdown'. I have never been so grateful for the freedom to work outdoors, and look for lost sheep in bluebell woods. Living and working on the farm gives an excellent quality of life, we are always busy and never bored, and always thinking of the next project, or the next generation of sheep. What more could you ask for from life?

Lockdown

For years people on social media
Have been criticizing me about
Farms being subsidized
Saying I shouldn't need
To take government money
To run my business

Now in lockdown
Those voices are silent
I wonder how many of those
Who have been so critical
Are now furloughed
Taking government money/

I hear no dissenting
Voices when the government
Says farmers are 'key workers'
Food supply chains are newsworthy
People seem to suddenly grasp
The fact that farmers produce food

Food is important
Supplies in supermarkets
Run low and I text home
Excitedly when I see flour
On the shelves
This is the new normal

Farmers are culturally relevant
The discussion is now
How to get the food we produce
To the consumers
Who are safely
Isolated in their homes

One of us here is shielded
'Extremely vulnerable'
A food parcel arrives
Full of essentials
Could we ever have imagined
This might happen in 2020?

There is talk of rationing
And at the end of this
I hope we remember
That upland farmers
Produce food as well
As ecosystem services

Socially Distant

The vet arrives
For a visit mid-lockdown
And I have in my mind
I must keep a cow's length
Of air between us
Socially distant

"Don't worry too much"
Says the vet
"You hill farmers
Are very low risk
You're always
Socially distant

"And I bet you've been
In voluntary lockdown
Every April
While you're lambing
For the last
Ten years."

Gathered

I am worried
As I watch the dates tick by
On the calendar
Of all the shows and meets
I should have been at
That I have witnessed
The end of something

The end of something
Very special
What if the shows
Cannot ever function
As they did?
What if 2019
Was the last shepherds meet?

I will let others
Worry about
Crashing economies and
Failing companies
My concern is
What if we never meet
To show sheep again?

I think back to
Stuffing rosettes
Into my jeans' pockets
And smiling into the
Winter sun arms aching
Holding sheep
In sticky mud

Somehow
These simple
Shepherds meets
Are what matter here.
They heft us to each other
Like a flock of old
Fell ewes being gathered in.

Gathered in
From our farms
Gathered together
To celebrate sheep
Held together
By generations
Of shepherding

Tied together
By working hands
With bailer twine
Sharing a way of life
Amongst the fells
Amongst the shepherds
Amongst the sheep.

Read More...

books by Andrea Meanwell

A Native Breed, Starting a Lake District Hill Farm, (2016)
978-1-910237-24-3

In My Boots, A Year on a Lake District Farm, (2017)
978-1-910237-24-3

Lakelanders: Stories and poems about living in a Lake District valley (2018)
978-1-910237-46-5

Four Seasons on a Westmorland Farm (2019)
978-1-910237-57-1